A Journal for All Seasons

Printed in Singapore.

ISBN 0-8118-0756-8

Book and cover design:
Tom Morgan, Blue Design

Distributed in Canada by Raincoast Books,
112 East Third Avenue, Vancouver, B.C. V5T 1C8

10 9 8 7 6 5 4 3 2 1

Chronicle Books
275 Fifth Street
San Francisco, CA 94103

A Journal for All Seasons

Photography by Deborah Schenck

Chronicle Books
San Francisco

The Earth is humanized
With quickening murmurs,
The swift, warm shadows of birds
and Spring's birth.

Mildred Emma Jones

OUR EARS WERE CLOSE TO THE WARM EARTH
WHERE EACH GRASS ROOT HELD THE
CHEERING LIFE.

GRANT LAMAR HOLLINGSHEAD

Upon a thousand hills the scarlet flame
Has touched each verdant tree, each
spreading shrub
And every wayside plant of countless name.

Mary Enola Rudolph

A DREAM OF LIGHT MORE SWEET
THAN PEACE OF NIGHT
WHERE LUSTROUS SHADOWS
FREEZE IN WINTER'S SIGHT.

PAUL WOLFF